The Refinement Process
WORKBOOK

BASED ON THE BOOK
THE REFINERY

Ronald Gibson

The Refinement Process Workbook

ISBN: 978-0-9962448-1-7

Published by Center Cross Creations

30 Waring Road, Rochester, NY 14609
www.TheRefinementProcess.com

Unless otherwise indicated, all Scripture is from the King James Version of the Holy Bible.

Scripture marked NKJV is taken from the New King James Version. Copyright 1982 by Thomas Nelson, Inc. Used by permission. All rights reserved.

Scripture marked NIV is taken from the New International Version. Copyright 1973, 1978,1984, 2011 by Biblica, Inc. Used by permission. All rights reserved worldwide.

Scripture marked NLT is taken from the New Living Translation. Copyright 1996, 2004, 2007 by Tyndale House Publishers, Inc. Used by permission. All rights reserved.

First Edition: October 2018

10 9 8 7 6 5 4 3 2 1

Please note that Center Cross Creations publisher's style capitalizes certain pronouns in Scripture that refer to the Father, Son, and the Holy Spirit. Boldface type in the Scripture quotations indicate the author's emphasis.

Printed in the United States of America

The Refinement Process Workbook

A Guide to Total Freedom from Drug Addictions

Based on the book

The Refinery

Overcoming Drug Addictions Through The

Supernatural Power Available To You

Contents

Preface

This workbook was created as a companion to my book, *The Refinery, Overcoming Drug Addictions Through The Supernatural Power Available To You*.

I wanted to make it more convenient for small groups, support groups and Bible study groups to engage in the material. Each phase of **The Refinement Process** is laid out with thoughtful content and action steps. The action steps can be done individually or in a group setting.

This workbook is designed to be written in. In addition, at the end of each chapter there are Note pages, so all your work will be in one handy place.

Before you begin the lessons, please do two things. First, be sure to read the Introduction. It will help you understand my thoughts and my core beliefs which are framed in this workbook.

Second, please, pray to the Lord concerning His desires for you. Ask the Lord for three things; Knowledge, Understanding and Wisdom. God is faithful to heal your body and cleanse you from all unrighteousness.

My hope for you is that you come to recognize and receive the supernatural power to break free from drug addictions.

NOTE: Perhaps you are not the one who is addicted to drugs. Perhaps it is a loved one; a son or daughter, a mother or father, a husband or wife. This course is still for you. The information contained herein this workbook will help you understand and support your loved one as you learn God's life changing power of deliverance.

Ronald Gibson

Introduction

Years ago, I worked with an addiction recovery ministry through my local church. There I counseled men and women who were hard-core drug addicts. While preparing to conduct counseling sessions, I looked back over my life and discovered the process that had brought about my deliverance from my years of drug addictions. I wrote down my discovery and used it as the basis for leading my weekly drug counseling sessions.

After years of living clean, free from drug addiction, I could share with my clients a more excellent way to become clean! I call it, **The Refinement Process**.

And be not conformed to this world: but you **be transformed by the renewing of your mind***, that you may prove what is that good, and acceptable, and perfect, will of God.*
Romans 12:2 (NIV)

The classic description of insanity is to continue doing the same thing over and over thinking that you will get a different result. Some of you have tried over and over to free yourself from the grip of addictions; but over and over you failed. That means that your way is not working. But, there are different way to succeed; try **The Refinement Process**.

In my case, as soon as I prayed for help, God helped me. That to me is amazing! That changed my way of thinking. I always thought that drug rehabilitation required a lengthy process which included painful detox, months in a residential rehab center (with the latest methods of psycho-therapeutic behavioral modification). Or, the possible use of replacement drug therapy, and a lifetime of sobriety support group meetings.

Many people have tried rehab centers to kick their drug addictions. Many have tried to maintain sobriety through 12-Step programs like AA or NA. If you are one of these people, and rehab or a 12-step program is working for you, I say GREAT. But, my research and personal experience has shown me that there are many people who try those methods and fail. There are alternative methods for eliminating addictions. **The Refinement Process** is a powerful alternative to live free from drug addiction.

There is no one-size-fits-all treatment for addictions. **The Refinement Process**, for many, is a more excellent way to achieve sobriety and live a healthier life. This is the process that worked for me and it has helped others whom I counseled. For those of you who are helpless and hopeless, there is help and there is hope.

You might be in a battle for your eternal soul and because of addictions, you're losing. In warfare, the army that triumphs is the one with superior fire-power. **The Refinement Process** will help you obtain the *supernatural fire-power* to defeat addictions, forever.

The Refinement Process

You don't change the old by resisting it. You change it by making it
obsolete through a superior methodology.
B. Fuller

Recovery versus Refinement

Many people have tried rehab centers to kick their drug addictions. Many have tried to maintain sobriety through 12-Step programs like AA or NA. If you are one of these people, and rehab or a 12-step program is working for you, I say GREAT. But, my research and personal experience has shown me that there are many people who try those methods and fail. There are alternative methods for eliminating addictions. **The Refinement Process** is a powerful alternative approach to living free from the grip of drug addiction.

There is no one-size-fits-all treatment for addictions. **The Refinement Process**, for many, is a more excellent way to achieve sobriety and live a healthier life. This is the process that worked for me and it has worked for others whom I have counseled. For those of you who are helpless and hopeless, there is help and hope.

Much of drug addiction treatment today is classified as *recovery treatment*. In this course you will learn about *refinement treatment*. Just what is the difference between recovery and refinement?

Recovery means to find or get back something or someone who is missing or lost. Recovery is the process whereby something or someone is returned to a former status. But, what if that former status was horrible? What if that former status was dysfunctional? What if that former status was miserable? Generally, when someone starts abusing drugs, it is because something is either wrong or missing in their life. So, what exactly is being recovered? Horror? Dysfunction? Misery?

The Refinement Process is a purging and purifying system. The results? A complete and thorough purification of your spirit, soul and body. Unlike a recovery methodology, **The Refinement Process** does not attempt to return you to a former status, rather, it guides you to new and improved status. The old impurities are removed; so, the end condition is better than the former condition.

Each human being is a unique individual person. You have your own personal victories and defeats, triumphs and tragedies, successes and failures. You have your own personal hopes, dreams and desires, as well as, your own personal hurts, nightmares and losses. **The Refinement Process** will work for each person; but, each person's reactions to the process will vary.

Generally, the length of time it takes to complete **The Refinement Process** is dependent upon your levels of acceptance and resistance. For some of you, your resistance is great. The greater the level of resistance, the slower the completion of the process. That means, the quicker you surrender to the processing, the quicker the completion of the process.

For some of you, **The Refinement Process** will work very quickly and completely. That is how it was for me. It worked so fast that it took me several weeks to realize that the work was completed. I was completely delivered from years of drug addiction.

Whichever way it works for you, whether quickly or slowly, **The Refinement Process** works!

The Five Phases

There are five phases. Each phase is designed to move you in systematic progression from drug dependence to drug independence. This is where your hard work is accomplished. Each Phase is a function of **The Refinement Process**.

> The Reflection Phase – Seeing Present Reality
> The Repentance Phase – Making a Directional Decision
> The Redemption Phase - Restoring Ownership
> The Recommitment Phase - Pledging Purity
> The Reemergence Phase - Becoming Visible Again

Now, let's get started. Welcome to **The Refinement Process**.

The Reflection Phase

Reflection: an image that is seen in a mirror or on a shiny surface; something that shows the effect, existence, or character of something else.

For now we see only a reflection as in a mirror; then we shall see face to face.
Now I know in part; then I shall know fully, even as I am fully known.
1 Corinthians 13:12

The Search Begins Now

The Reflection Phase is the first important phase in **The Refinement Process**. If you do not take this step, then you can go no farther. This is foundational. If you are serious about gaining your freedom from addictions, then you MUST take and complete this crucial step. If you are ready to become cleansed and pure, then let's get moving. Step out!

You are The Person in the Mirror

"What do you want to be when you grow up?"

Did anyone ask you that question when you were a kid? The list of youngsters' answers might include being a doctor, a lawyer, a teacher, a coach, a fireman, a policeman and on and on. The one thing you never hear a kid say is, "I want to grow up to be a junkie!"

Let's take a couple of Action Steps that will help you to reflect on who you are, where you have been and where you are going.

Reflection Step 1 – Childhood Photos

Find one of your childhood photos, preferably a snapshot or a school picture when you were five or six years old. Find one that was taken during your age of innocence. Now look at that face; really exam it. That was your face. Were you smiling? Did your eyes twinkle? That is the face of innocence and purity. Wouldn't it be great to return to a state of innocence? Wouldn't it be great to be pure once again? You may be thinking, "That's impossible, look at me now. I'm a wreck. I'm too far gone."

I say, NO! You are never too far gone. There is a way back to the innocence and purity of that young child. He or she is still alive in you. You owe it to that child in you, to return to a state of purity. It starts with reflection.

Now, take your childhood picture and tape it to the corner of your bathroom mirror. Make it the wallpaper photo on your tablet, laptop or smartphone. Use it as a constant reminder of your journey back to innocence and purity.

Part of every misery is, so to speak, the misery's shadow or reflection: the fact that you don't merely suffer but have to keep on thinking about the fact that you suffer. I not only live each endless day in grief, but live each day thinking about living each day in grief.
C.S. Lewis

Reflection, Your Starting Point for Refinement

There is a progression that starts with reflection and leads to refinement.

> Reflection ➔ Recognition – Begin to see things that you recognize.
> Recognition ➔ Realization – Become aware of what is real.
> Realization ➔ Resignation – Become resigned to change.
> Resignation ➔ Refinement – Become "fine" once gain (refined).

You look in the mirror to examine your face; now look at your life and examine the condition of your soul. Your life reflects your heart and your character. Have you ever taken a glance at your heart? That is called *soul searching*. It is amazing what you will find when you take the time to look.

Let's look at this progression. You already know that reflection is something that shows the effect, existence, or character of something else. When you reflect on something or someone you begin to recognize things about that object or person. **Reflection leads to recognition.**

Recognition is the act of knowing who or what someone or something is based upon previous knowledge or experience. Recognition is important because it helps you become familiar with the subject of the reflection. It is like when you run into someone that you have not seen in many years. At first, you may not know who the person is, but then he says or does something that causes you to recognize him. **Recognition leads to realization.**

Realization is the state of understanding or becoming aware of something. It could also be defined as the act of achieving something that was planned or hoped for. Let's continue with the example of the person that you had not seen in many years. Once you recognize him, you may realize that you lent him money and he never repaid you. Further, you may realize a full repayment of the debt. First, you realized, (became aware of) the person and the fact that he owed you money. Second, you realized, (something that you hoped for), the repayment of the debt when he handed you the money owed. **Realization leads to resignation.**

Resignation is the feeling that something unpleasant is going to happen and cannot be changed. It's also the act of giving up a job or position in a formal or official way. The word resignation has the same root as the word signature, which means to endorse or write off something. Maybe, due to your drug addiction, you resigned yourself to the thought that you will always be an addict. Maybe you have signed off on your hopes for a better life without drugs.

Resignation is like a two-sided coin; each side has opposing viewpoints which lead to vastly different results. On the one side, resignation can present a negative view of unpleasant, unchangeable things. If you are not careful, you might resign yourself to the thought *Things are so bad, why even bother to try to change?*

On the other side of the coin, resignation can present a positive view. Perhaps it could be the resigning from an old, unfulfilling lifestyle with the thought, *I'm signing off on my bondage to drugs!* One resignation tends toward signing off on positive lifestyle changes; the other resignation tends toward signing off on destruction and defeat.

That type of **resignation leads to refinement**. Refinement should be the desired results you seek. When you resign yourself to refinement, you will begin to see better results. Now, you can sign off on drug addiction and sign up for purity and the freedom from drug addiction.

Let's Face It

Many years ago, while I was addicted to drugs, I looked in the mirror; I saw the face of death staring back at me. My face was thin and gaunt, my complexion was ashy, my eyes looked lifeless. I didn't recognize my face in the mirror. But, that was just the beginning of my transformation from death to life.

As water reflects the face, so one's life reflects the heart.
Proverbs 27:19 NIV

One day, you too, will face the person in your mirror. You don't know the hour or the day that it will happen for you. Maybe you are not ready for your date with the person in the mirror. I do know that when you are ready to truly face the person in the mirror, you will be ready for your transformation. When you are ready, that face in your mirror will plead with you for help. It will be your date with a brighter future, your future of freedom! But, first you must face it.

Face the Facts: stop putting on a mask;
Face the Fears: stop lying to yourself; you can be free.
Face the Folly: stop the foolishness.

Search me, O God, and know my heart: test me and know my anxious thoughts:
See if there is any offensive way in me, and lead me in the way everlasting.
Psalms 139:23

Generally, before you go out in public, you probably look in the mirror. Just a quick glance reveals anything about your appearance which might be out of order like hair not combed, facial blemishes, teeth not brushed, clothing mismatched, blouse unbuttoned, or slacks unzipped. Isn't it better to catch a view of that before you go out in public?

So then, after some adjustments, the mirror shows you that you look great. People judge you by your outward appearance. And although it is important to keep up appearances, you must be mindful of your inward appearance, too.

It has been said that the eyes are the windows of the soul. When you look into the mirror, look into your eyes. Do you recognize the person in the reflection? How do you reflect on the inner you? Let's take a look.

Reflection Step 2 – The Mirror Test

Use the following questions as an inner mirror; a mirror for your soul. As you reflect on your answers, know that there may be another perspective; another point of view that you do not see. Be honest with yourself as you gaze into this *soul* mirror.

As you search yourself, look for scars. Reflect on the wounds which were self-inflicted as well as those inflicted by other people. Look for things that are obvious. Look for things that are hidden deep inside. Take time now to search yourself and find some answers. Be sure to write down your answers. You will need these written answers later.

Ask yourself:

Who am I?

_____

_____

_____

Why am I alive?

_____

_____

_____

How did I get my life into this condition?

_____

_____

_____

What will be my future?

_____

_____

_____

To see where you are going, you should know where you are. When you use a GPS to get the directions to your destination, it starts by determining your current location. The Refiner starts by assaying the gold or silver ore to determine the current condition and the possible value of the finished metal.

Have you ever seen an infomercial for a new diet or exercise program? To support their claims of fabulous results, the sponsor always shows the BEFORE and

AFTER photos. The after photo always looks much better than the before photo. There must be a way to see the results; otherwise, why buy their program? People want to see results.

In **The Refinement Process**, you want to see results. So, let's take a BEFORE and AFTER snapshot.

Ask yourself two questions (be sure to write down your answers):

Only you can answer what your life was like before the entrance of drugs. Were you contented or confused? Were you satisfied or dissatisfied? Were you happy or miserable? It is important to identify your pre-addiction state of being. Many people choose drugs to self-medicate their hurtful, miserable or unsatisfactory conditions.

1. What was my life like before I started using drugs?

_____

_____

_____

_____

_____

Now, consider all the possibilities for your life once you are freed from the chains that prevent you from realizing your full potential. Consider a healthier body or a wealthier lifestyle, since all your money is not being wasted on addictions. Consider restored relationships with your family. Consider new relationships with exciting new friends.

2. What can my life be like after drugs are gone?

_____

_____

_____

_____

_____

Reflection Step 3 – Take a "Selfie"

That's right! If you have a mobile device or tablet, take a selfie. Pictures have a way of showing the true you. It is said, "one picture says a thousand words." Be sure to save it; you will need it later in this course.

Notes

_____

_____

_____

_____

_____

_____

_____

_____

_____

_____

_____

_____

_____

_____

_____

_____

_____

_____

_____

Notes

_____

_____

_____

_____

_____

_____

_____

_____

_____

_____

_____

_____

_____

_____

_____

_____

_____

_____

_____

_____

_____

_____

_____

The Repentance Phase

Repentance: deep sorrow, compunction, or contrition for a past sin, wrongdoing, or the like; regret for a past action.

When you repent, you admit your faults and ask for forgiveness.

Standing at the Crossroads

You made it through the Reflection Phase and now you have arrived here at the Repentance Phase. Having made it this far, you now are at a decision point. You are standing at a crossroads.

There is the road that continues in the way that you have been going, drug abuse, heartache, shame, and loss of family and friends. That road is a dead-end leading to the destruction of your life and premature death. But, there is a road that crosses that road, a different road that leads you to an addiction-free life. You are at that place of decision, the crossroads.

There is a way that appears to be right,
but in the end it leads to death. Proverbs 14:12

Let's take an Action Step.

Repentance Step 1 – The Celebrity List

Philip Seymour Hoffman, Heath Ledger, Whitney Houston, Amy Winehouse, Michael Jackson and Prince, these are just a handful of the many famous people who recently died of drug overdoses. They had remarkable talent, wealth and fame. The tragedy is that they all probably had more movies, songs and performances that they could have contributed to our lives and culture. Their stories might help you to reconsider the path for your own life.

Make your own list of celebrities whose untimely deaths were the results of drug or alcohol addiction (or drug/alcohol related). Do an internet search of "celebrity deaths by overdose."

List ten celebrities that died in the past ten years.

1._____

2._____

3._____

4._____

5._____

6._____

7._____

8._____

9._____

10._____

Pick two from your list with whom you closely identify; have a photo of each person.

Now internet search the life stories of both celebrities. Read each celebrity's life story.

Write down the things that are similar with your life story: broken family, abandonment, divorce, early death of a loved one, poor choice of friends, any kind of physical, emotional or sexual abuse, mental health issues, negative attitudes or destructive behaviors.

Similar to me:

_____

_____

_____

_____

Write down how the celebrities each coped with their troubles.

How they coped:

_____

_____

_____

_____

_____

Now write down how you are coping with your own troubles.

How I coped:

_____

_____

_____

_____

_____

Did you find some similarities with the celebrity's journey and your journey? Are you trying to cope with your addictions in the same way they coped with theirs? A wise person learns from the mistakes of other people and adjusts his own actions thereby avoiding a similar tragic destiny.

> _Do not conform to the pattern of this world, but be_
> _transformed by the renewing of your mind._
> Romans 12:2

For many people, the three words that are hardest to say are, _I was wrong_. Or even, _I am sorry_. You may not like to admit failure or defeat. You may not like to admit that your actions caused damage or injury to someone else.

Usually, that is because of your own foolish pride. You want to appear that you have everything under control, when something has you under its control. Drugs are not only considered *controlled substances*, they are also controlling substances. Your life may be out of your control.

Let's take another Action Step.

Repentance Step 2 – I am sorry, Forgive me

Have you ever felt sorry for your actions? Not just sorry because you got caught, but sorry because you were wrong. Have you ever confessed to the person that you wronged and asked them to forgive you?

> *Therefore confess your sins to each other and pray for each other so that you may be healed. The prayer of a righteous person is powerful and effective.*
> James 5:16

In this exercise you will write five "I am sorry" statements. Say what it is that you did for which you are sorry. Also write the person's name to whom you are sorry.

1. I am sorry for _____;
   Name_____

2. I am sorry for _____;
   Name_____

3. I am sorry for_____;
   Name_____

4. I am sorry for_____;
   Name_____

5. I am sorry for _____;
   Name_____

Now you will write five "Forgive me" statements. List the person's name from above and state the offense for which you are asking forgiveness.

1. Name _____;

    Forgive me for _____, I repent.

2. Name _____;

    Forgive me for _____, I repent.

3. Name _____;

    Forgive me for _____, I repent
    .

4. Name _____;

    Forgive me for _____, I repent.

5. Name _____;

    Forgive me for _____, I repent.

The purpose for this step is so that you can get use to admitting your faults and repenting.

Repentance occurs when you admit your current state of being. You admit that you have made a mess of your life. You admit that you are unable to stop your downward freefall. Be big enough to admit your addictions and look for help in overcoming them. Help is here in the Repentance Phase. Let's continue!

You Need a Course Correction

> *We all want progress, but if you're on the wrong road, progress means doing an about-turn and walking back to the right road; in that case, the man who turns back soonest is the most progressive.*
>
> C.S. Lewis

We have all, at one time, found ourselves going down the road heading in the wrong direction. Drug addiction is that road which leads to a dead end. It is time for you to turn around. It is time for you to change your course. Get on the right road; it leads to a great new life.

The Refiner said, *"I am the way, the truth, and the life…"* John 14:6

Get on the right road, going the right way. Ignorance occurs when you turn your back on the truth. By ignoring the truth, you set yourself up to be deceived. When you turn your back to The Refiner, you are heading in the wrong way.

When you turn *toward* The Refiner, you turn your back on the past hurts, the past troubles, the past disappointments. You can then face the solution for your messed-up life. The Refiner IS the solution to your problems. He IS the supernatural power you need to overcome your addictions. He can rescue you, if you let Him.

The ore cannot refine itself; it takes The Refiner to purify it.

Now, let's find out more about The Refiner and understand how He brings power to The Refinement Process.

Who is The Refiner?

The Refiner

He sat by the fire of seven-fold heat,
As He watched by the precious ore.
And closer He bent with a searching gaze
As He heated it more and more.
He knew He had ore that could stand the test
And He wanted the finest gold,
To mold as a crown for the King to wear,
Set with gems of price untold.
So He laid our gold in the burning fire,
Though we fain would have said Him, "Nay."
And He watched the dross that we had not seen,
As it melted and passed away.
And the gold grew brighter, and yet more bright
And our eyes were so dim with tears.
As we saw the fire, not the Master's hand,
And questioned with anxious fear.
Yet our gold shone out with a richer glow,
As it mirrored a Form above
That bent o'er the fire, though unseen by us
With a look of infinite love.
Can we think that it pleases His loving heart
To cause a moment of pain?
Ah, no, but He saw through the present cross
The bliss of eternal gain.
So He waited there with a watchful eye,
With a love that is strong and sure,
And His gold did not suffer a bit more heat
Than was needed to make it pure!

Source Unknown

Throughout the Scripture, Jesus is referred to in many ways. He is described as the Good Shepherd, the Captain of the Host (army), the Son of Man, the Son of God, the Master, the Sower, the Teacher, the Healer, and much more.

Now I want you to recognize Jesus as The Refiner imagine your soul as the raw gold ore. He is the One who will remove your impurities (drugs) and refine your soul; so you come out as pure 24 karat gold!

Not Religion, It's About Relationship

When I mentioned Jesus, did you immediately think of religion? Most people do. But, Jesus never came to create a religion. He announced His plans:

> *The Spirit of the Lord is on me, because he has anointed me to proclaim good news to the poor. He has sent me to proclaim freedom for the prisoners and recovery of sight for the blind, to set the oppressed free, to preach the acceptable year of the Lord.*
> Luke 4:18-19

Jesus came for the poor, the brokenhearted, the captives, the blind, and those who are bruised. His only message for you is that the Kingdom of God has come for your benefit.

So, if Jesus did not come to establish religion, why did He come to us? He came to re-establish mankind's relationship with God. Not religion (mankind's attempt to reach God), but instead *relationship* (God's desire to have a royal family).

Jesus came for the Refinement of mankind.
He came to us as The Refiner.

Find No Offense in Him

So now you recognize The Refiner. You may not know Him, but you are coming to know who He is. The Refiner of your soul is Jesus, the Christ! He is the only one who has the power and the willingness to rescue and refine you. There is none other.

This may not be what you want to hear, but you need to hear it and accept it. See what The Refiner says to you,

And blessed is he, whosoever shall not be offended in me. Luke 7:23

Notice that He said **whosoever.** That means you! He said blessed is he who is not offended because of Him. Some of you will be offended by the mention of His name. If that is you, the question is:

Is your offense of Jesus greater than
your desire to be free from drug addictions?

Think about it. What is more important to you, your offense over Jesus being The Refiner **or** continuing to be dragged to your destruction by addictions which have control over you?

The Refiner states the person who is not offended in Him *is blessed*. So, if that is true then the opposite is also true; the person who *is* offended in Him is cursed! And that is what addictions are, a curse!

What The Refiner is asking of you is such a small thing, especially compared to what He will do for you and what He will do inside of you. He will cleanse you; He will purify you; He will forgive you. He will release you from drug addictions.

Jesus, The Refiner, was perfect in every way. He never sinned. Neither did He do any wrong.

God made him who had no sin to be sin for us, so that in
him we might become the righteousness of God.
2 Corinthians 5:21

Jesus lived a perfect, sin-free life; therefore, He was the perfect sacrifice so that we could have atonement for our sins. He was crucified. He died nailed to a wooden cross. He was buried in a tomb. But, on the third day, He was empowered to rise from the dead.

The Refiner has unlimited power. He is making it available for you right now. But, for Him to use that power to refine you, you must admit that you are powerless to change yourself. That's what **The Refinement Process** is all about. Repent and admit that you need The Refiner's powerful help. When you accept His help, He will use His power to raise you up from your deadly addictions. Accept Him as The Refiner.

> *The first condition is repentance, which means a change of mind. Formerly I thought sin a pleasant thing, but now I have changed my mind about it; formerly I thought the world an attractive place, but now I know better; formerly I regarded it a miserable business to be a Christian, but now I think differently. Once I thought certain things delightful, now I think them vile; once I thought other things utterly worthless, now I think them most precious. That is a change of mind, and that is repentance.*
> Watchman Nee

What You Must Do to be Refined

When you come to the place where you admit that you cannot change yourself, then you are ready for The Refiner to work on you.

If you are not ready to repent, no one can convince or persuade you. The Refiner is patiently waiting for you to complete this Repentance Phase.

At this point in the Repentance Phase, you might ask, "What must I do to be rescued, refined and purified?" Let's look at how The Refiner answers that question.

> *Very truly I tell you, no one can see the kingdom of God unless they are born again.*
> John 3:3 (NIV)

He went on to explain the purpose and promises of refinement,

> *For God so loved the world that he gave his one and only Son, that whoever believes in him shall not perish but have eternal life. For God did not send his Son into the world to condemn the world,* **but to save the world through him.**
> John 3:16-17 (NIV)

The key to the Repentance Phase can be found in Paul's letter to the people of Rome.

If you declare with your mouth, "Jesus is Lord," and believe in your heart that God raised him from the dead, you will be saved. For it is with your heart that you believe and are justified, and it is with your mouth that you profess your faith and are saved. As Scripture says, "Anyone who believes in him will never be put to shame."

Romans 10:9-11 (NIV)

Now, if you are ready, prayer the following prayer:

Deliverance Prayer

Lord Jesus, my Refiner, I know that I am a sinner, and I am sorry for my sin. I repent of it and I turn to You by faith right now. I believe that You are the Son of God. Thank You for dying on the cross for me and paying the price for my sins. I ask You to come into my life now and be my Rescuer and my Refiner. I surrender myself to You. Refine me and help me to live my life for You. Thank You, Lord. In Jesus name I pray. Amen

---

If you prayed that prayer and truly believe in Jesus as your Lord, Congratulations! Welcome to The Refiner's family! You just made the best decision that you will ever make. Get ready, my friend, for the biggest, best change of your life. You are staged to go from impurity to purity; from imperfection to perfection.

When purity of spirit comes, then that which is impure passes away. When perfection of spirit comes, then that which is imperfect passes away. Purity and perfection of spirit, through The Refiner, always trumps impurity and imperfection!

You have already done some of the hard stuff, but your power is limited.

From here on The Refiner will do most of the heavy lifting, His power is limitless.

Notes

_____

_____

_____

_____

_____

_____

_____

_____

_____

_____

_____

_____

_____

_____

_____

_____

_____

_____

_____

_____

_____

_____

_____

_____

Notes

The Redemption Phase

Redemption: the act of making something better or more acceptable; the act of exchanging something for money; an award, etc.

For you were bought at a price; therefore glorify God in your body
and in your spirit, which are God's
1 Corinthians 6:20

You have just passed through the Repentance Phase. Presently, some of the biggest impurities in your life are your addictions. Hopefully, by now, you have admitted it and asked for The Refiner's help to rescue and refine you.

Welcome! You have arrived at the Redemption Phase. This is the most exciting and remarkable Phase in **The Refinement Process**. Up to now, you were in control of things. You had to reflect; you recognized your helpless and hopeless condition. You had to Repent; you admitted that you could not change yourself and you needed The Refiner's powerful help.

You made it through those Phases. From here on, The Refiner takes over. Your part is to trust, believe, and obey His directions. Now it is time for The Refiner to begin His work on you.

Kidnapped and Held For Ransom

Because of sin, all of mankind was abducted by an enemy, Satan. He kidnapped us from the real life which God planned. We were held hostage until our ransom was paid. As you saw, there was only one person qualified to pay our ransom. That person is The Refiner, Jesus.

The Redemption Phase is where you acknowledge and accept that your ransom is paid. Through His death (on the cross), His burial (three days in the grave) and His resurrection, He defeated Satan. The Refiner made payment for your release,

release from the addictions. The Refiner paid it in full with His life. He gave His life a ransom for many.

The moment that you repented, The Refiner released you from your debt. He gave His life as a ransom for you and me. Your debt was paid and now you are free!

Free Delivery, Paid In Full

At this point you will need some basic background to understand the magnificent work that is occurring in you; and the work truly is magnificent. There are some basic truths that will help you appreciate your total deliverance from drug addictions.

Redemption is deliverance because of the payment of a price

Think of the term deliverance; it is the movement from one place to another. Mail is delivered from the sender's location to the recipient's address. Freight is shipped from a warehouse and delivered to a factory or store. Products are delivered from an online retailer to your home.

Perhaps you heard the phrase, *deliverance from drugs* or *deliverance from addictions*. It means that a person moves from one location to another. The addiction goes away; it leaves. That sounds crazy. It sounds impossible, but God can do the impossible.

When you give your letters or packages to the postal worker, that person takes them away to be delivered to the addressee. That mail is picked up and delivered from you to another place. Through the supernatural power of The Refiner, which is available to you, drugs and addictions can be picked up and taken away and delivered back to hell (where they came from and where they belong).

Many times, when you see an advertisement on television or on the internet, the seller will offer free shipping and handling, or free delivery. That is an added incentive to buy their product.

In truth, there is no free delivery; it simply does not exist. Somebody always pays. And that somebody is you! The seller simply calculated his shipping costs into the price that is charged to you. It appears that you aren't paying extra delivery charges, but you are.

In contrast, when The Refiner delivers you from drug addictions, there is no additional cost to you. That's right, you pay no extra delivery charges. But, remember, there is no free delivery. In the case of your deliverance, somebody paid the price. That somebody was Christ, The Refiner. The delivery charges were included in the redemption package, paid in full by The Refiner for you. You receive it without paying anything, but it cost Him everything! He gave His all so that you could go free.

Redemption is rescue from the grip of addictions, and much, much more. Through your drug addictions and other destructive acts, you incurred a sin debt to God. It is a debt that you can never repay. Jesus The Refiner paid a debt, your debt that He did not owe. How and why did He pay the price to free you?

How did He pay it? - He paid your debt with His own blood. He was beaten, tortured and executed for you. The magnitude of our sin was so great that it required His perfect sacrifice to pay it off.

> *In fact, according to the law of Moses, nearly everything was purified*
> *with blood. For without the shedding of blood, there is no forgiveness.*
> Hebrews 9:22 (NLT)

Because Jesus, The Refiner, lived a perfect life, free from sin, His sacrificial death was not for His own sin, but it was for ours - yours, mine and the sins of all the peoples of the world.

> *In him we have **redemption** through his blood, the forgiveness of sins, in*
> *accordance with the riches of God's grace that he lavished on us. With*
> *all wisdom and understanding…*
> Ephesians 1:7-8

Why did He pay it? - The Refiner did it because of His awesome love for you. He loves you more than you love yourself. He did it so you can live a successful life, free from drug addictions. He has already done the hard part. Now, can you sense Him working on your heart and your head? He is cleansing you from the inside out. The Refiner told us:

> *…I am come that they might have life, and that they might have* it *more abundantly.*
> John 10:10b

God loved you first.
God loved you best.
God loved you completely

And, it is not because we deserved it. In fact, we did not deserve anything that He did for us. There is nothing that we can do to deserve His great love. We simply receive it, accept it and give Him thanks for it. God recognized that we were unable to free ourselves, therefore He sent a Redeemer.

No creature that deserved Redemption would need to be redeemed. They that are whole need not the physician. Christ died for men precisely because men are not worth dying for; to make them worth it.
C.S. Lewis

What Does He See When He Looks At Me?

Often, there is a stark contrast between what you see in yourself and what The Refiner sees when He looks at you. You see your impurities and imperfections; The Refiner sees you purified and perfected. You see past failures; He sees your potential for greatness! Let's look at this as you take another Action Step forward.

Time for an Action Step.

Redemption Step 1 – The Refiner's View of You

Go back to the Reflection Phase and locate the Reflection Step 2. There you wrote your answers to five important questions. Your answers are a self-assessment of *the who, the what, and the why of your life*. Remember, The Refiner also has an opinion of you.

It is found in the Scriptures. Let's see how He answers those same questions concerning you. Now, let's compare your point of view with The Refiner's point of view:

1. What does The Refiner say about who I am?

He said you were *created in His image and likeness*…Genesis 1:26

He said you are *fearfully and wonderfully made!* Psalms 139:14

In Reflection Step 2, What did you say about who you are?

_____

_____

_____

2. What does The Refiner say about why am I alive?

He said you are *created for His pleasure*... Psalms 149:4.

He said you are to *be fruitful, multiply, replenish the world, subdue it and have dominion over His creation.* Genesis 1:28

In Reflection Step 2, What did you say about why you are alive?

_____

_____

_____

3. What does The Refiner say about how I got in my present condition?

He said *there is a path before each person that seems right, but it ends in death.* Proverbs 14:12 (NLT)

In Reflection Step 2, What did you say about how you are in your present condition?

_____

_____

_____

4. What does The Refiner say about what will be my future?

He said *you shall reign with Him forever*... Revelation 22:5 (NKJV)

In Reflection Step 2, What did you say about what will be your future?

_____

_____

_____

How do your answers compare with The Refiner's answers? Your answers may reflect helplessness or hopelessness. His answers reflect His helpfulness towards you and His hope for you to have a better future.

The Boy Who Lost His Boat [1]

Tom carried his new toy boat to the edge of the river. He carefully placed it in the water and slowly let out the string. How smoothly the boat sailed! Tom sat in the warm sunshine, admiring the little boat that he had built. Suddenly a strong current caught the boat. Tom tried to pull it back to shore, but the string broke. The little boat raced downstream.

Tom ran along the sandy shore as fast as he could. But his little boat soon slipped out of sight. All afternoon he searched for the boat. Finally, when it was too dark to look any longer, Tom sadly went home.

A few days later, on the way home from school, Tom spotted a boat just like his in a store window. When he got closer, he could see -- sure enough -- it was his! Tom hurried to the store manager. "Sir, that's my boat in your window! I made it!"

"Sorry, son, but someone else brought it in this morning. If you want it, you'll have to buy it for ten dollars."

Tom ran home and counted all his money. Exactly ten dollars! When he reached the store, he rushed to the counter. "Here's the money for my boat." As he left the store, Tom hugged his boat and said, "Now you're twice mine. First, I made you and now I bought you."

In creation, He made you. In redemption, He bought you back!

Redemption Step 2 – Create Your New Vision Statement

Based on The Refiner's perspective of you that you discovered in Redemption Step 1, let's summarize:

You are fearfully and wonderfully created in His image and in His likeness.

You are created to for His pleasure.

---

[1] Good News Publishers, Westchester, IL.

You are to avoid dead-end roads which appear to be the right way.

You are created to reign with Him throughout eternity.

You are created to be productive and powerful; to be fruitful, multiply, replenish, subdue and have dominion over His creation.

Now, let's put this all together to create a power Vision Statement for your everyday life and your future. Write your name on the blank lines.

My Personal Vision Statement

I _____ *am fearfully and wonderfully created by God to look like Him and to act like Him. He created me for His pleasure.*

I _____ *am created to be productive and powerful.*

I _____ *will be fruitful, multiply the resources of my fruitfulness, then use those multiplied resources for the benefit of other people.*

My Refiner is always with me and He always points me to the right path. Through Him, I _____ make use of the supernatural power available to me.

Print it on a poster and tape it on your mirror. Write this Vision Statement on a card and carry it with you in your wallet or purse. Read it and speak it often.

This statement is the essence of who you are and why you are on this planet! You exist to bring glory to God. This is the reason why The Refiner wants to refine you. And this will last forever, if you are redeemed by The Refiner's blood.

Wow! **The Refinement Process** has been a truly amazing journey. But we are not through yet. There are still two critical Phases through which you must pass. Can you start to see and feel the results of The Refiner's hands upon you? You are made FREE!

During the Reflection Phase and Repentance Phase you were in charge. First, you saw a reflection of the real you. Second, you went on to confess your iniquities (impurities) and asked for forgiveness and deliverance from your addictions.

In the Redemption Phase, The Refiner took charge. He turned up The Refinery fire to cleanse you from all unrighteousness and release you from the chains of your addictions. He sacrificed His own life so that you could have a more abundant and eternal life.

Next, in the Recommitment Phase you are back in charge. The completeness of your deliverance will be your responsibility and it will require your firm commitments. You must fill your new life with the things which please God.

Review your **Personal Vision Statement** that you just completed. You must make it the blue-print for constructing your successful, meaningful, purposeful life. It will be challenging, but with your powerful Refiner always present, you have all you need to succeed. The Refiner's purpose combined with your plan, that's a winning combo.

Notes

_____

_____

_____

_____

_____

_____

_____

_____

_____

_____

_____

_____

_____

_____

_____

_____

_____

_____

_____

_____

_____

_____

Notes

The Recommitment Phase

Recommitment: to commit again.

Let's start this phase with an Action Step.

Recommitment Step 1 – Integrity; How good is your word?

Start by taking a quick inventory. Please take a few moments to answer the following questions:

1. Describe the last time you broke a promise?

_____

_____

_____

2. Describe the last time you kept a promise?

_____

_____

_____

3. Is it easier for you to tell the truth or to lie?

_____

4. What must you do to remain committed to The Refiner?

_____

_____

Guard Your Heart for Out of It
Flows the Streams of Your Life

Stay on Course – Stay Committed

It is extremely important that you stay committed to The Refiner. **The Refinement Process** is here to help you do that. Without commitment, your power to stay the course will be diminished. It was Jesus who rescued you; it will be Jesus that keeps you safe during impending pains and persecutions. He has promised to never leave you nor forget about you.

The Refiner is that constant help that you will need to succeed in your new addiction free life. Think back on the mess that you created for yourself in the past. Now that you are being delivered from your past failures, it is crucial that you maintain your victorious life without drugs. The Recommitment Phase will help you in this maintenance.

You will be facing many trials, testings and temptations. Your natural body will have a longing to go back to the old ways. You are in the process of cleansing and purification; and, yet, your mind and body will sometimes long for past drug highs. You must remember how low those drug highs brought you.

As a dog returns to its vomit, so fools repeat their folly.
Proverbs 26:11 NIV

It's time for you to recommit to yourself and to your loved ones. In this process of recommitment, you will need to *de-commit* to your old negative people, places and so-called pleasures. There are two types of commitments, or, maybe, it might be better said two directions of commitments, horizontal and vertical. Let's look at how these commitments affect your new life.

Horizontal and Vertical Commitments

The word horizontal is defined as: *relating to, directed toward, or consisting of individuals or entities of similar status or on the same level.* The word vertical is defined as: *situated at the highest point.* But, what does that have to do with commitments? Let's examine this concept.

Horizontal Commitments are your commitments to people on your same level. These are the commitments that you make to your friends and family, your co-workers or your fellow students. These are what could be called peer to peer commitments.

Horizontal Commitments also refer to the type of commitment between married couples and soul-mates. Sororities and fraternities, civic groups (Rotary or Lions), fraternal orders (Elks, Shriners or Masons) all require high standards of commitment. Horizontal Commitments are reciprocal. You commit to others and you expect the same degree of commitment from them in return.

On the other side, Vertical Commitments are your commitments to those people of higher authority. These are the commitments that you make to your parents, your workplace supervisor, your teachers or professors, and your pastor or spiritual leaders.

Vertical Commitments are the basis of what is known as the chain of command. You see it in all branches of the military and in business enterprises both small and large. People all answer to those of a higher ranking or a higher authority. And again, just like with Horizontal Commitments, Vertical Commitments are reciprocal. There is an expectation of commitment from those of lower ranking as well as those of higher ranking.

The highest Vertical Commitments of all are those that we make to Jesus The Refiner. We commit ourselves to love, honor and obey Him. We commit ourselves to let His will have priority over our will. Jesus said it best when He prioritized the will of His Heavenly Father over His own will; He said, *Father, if thou be willing, remove this cup from me* (referring to Christ's mission to redeem us by His death on a cross).

He went on to say, *nevertheless not my will but thine be done.* It was the ultimate Vertical Commitment, and it should be our pledge to God our heavenly Father; **not my will, but your will be done**. That becomes proof of your devotion to Him.

Higher Levels of Commitment Require
Deeper Levels of Devotion to God

Your commitment to The Refiner is your most important commitment of all. The Refiner gave you His promises. Keep your word to Him by remembering His word to you.

Vowing a Vow

Your commitment is your promise, your pledge, your oath, your word, your vow. The words pledge, oath, and vow are synonymous. They represent an oral contract of performance. A vow is a spoken agreement between two or more people. Vowing a vow is the act of pledging or promising that you will do something for the person.

There are many examples of vowing a vow. You see it when a politician takes the Oath of Office, vowing to be a leader for his constituents. When you Pledge Allegiance to the flag, you vow to be loyal to the United States of America.

When couples exchange wedding vows, they promise to be faithful and care for each other. Priests might take a vow of celibacy, or a vow of poverty or a vow of silence, all to bring them closer to God. Vows are the basis of a commitment that binds together relationships.

A vow is constructed of four basic building blocks – the People, the Pledge, the Prize and the Payment. You can see that it is like any business or personal transaction. Whether it's a sales contract or its loaning money to a friend, a vow incorporates the 4 Ps: the People, the Pledge, the Prize and the Payment. Let's examine this further.

The People are the two or more persons that come into an agreement in the vow. On one side, the person(s) who vow the vow (make the pledge). On the other side, the person(s) provide the prize, (the desired results or desired object.)

The Pledge is simply your word. When vowing a vow your pledge is your verbal promise to accomplish something in exchange for a desired results or desired object. In most cases the vow is verbal, spoken in the presence of the other person with whom you agree.

The Prize is the object of your desire or the results that you desired in exchange for the payment of your vows.

The Payment is the actual performance of the pledge. The person making the vow must do the thing which he or she pledged.

This whole process can be understood in the following example. *I pledge allegiance to the flag of the United States of America, and to the republic for which it stands: one nation under God, indivisible, with liberty and justice for all.* From classrooms and school auditoriums to political rallies and major sports events, many people address the Stars and Stripes and repeat this vow. Look at the 4 Ps in this example.

- The People – citizens of the United States of America
- The Pledge – allegiance to the flag and the republic
- The Prize – one indivisible nation with liberty and justice for all
- The Payment – devotion to this nation and an obligation to be loyal to it

Generally, the prize is given before the payment is made. When, as the result of a vow, the prize is provided, then there is an expectation of the payment. If the prize is received and the payment is not performed, there is injustice and imbalance. A person enjoys gain while the other person suffers loss.

The Lord, our Refiner requires justice and balance in your relationships. He takes vows very seriously. He expects fulfillment of the pledge and payment for prize.

That which has gone from your lips you shall keep and perform, for you voluntarily vowed to the LORD your God what you have promised with your mouth.
Deuteronomy 23:23 (NKJV)

When you make a vow to God, do not delay to pay it;
For He has no pleasure in fools. Pay what you have vowed - Better not to vow than to vow and not pay. Do not let your mouth cause your flesh to sin…
Ecclesiastes 5:4-6a (NKJV)

A word to the wise concerning vows; if you can't pay it, then don't say it. Always pay your vows.

Time for another Action Step forward,

Recommitment Step 2 – Creating My Vow

Now let's try your hand at vowing a vow. Make it simple and doable; don't promise something that is not within your ability to perform.

Prepare a vow to The Refiner. Think of one simple vow to the Lord.

Print the vow. Print or write out your vow.

Proclaim the vow. Verbally state the pledge to the Lord to whom you make the vow.

Post the vow. Find a prominent place in your home to post your vow.

My Lord, (my pledge to Him)

_____

_____

_____

My Lord, (His prize to you)

_____

_____

_____

My Lord, for receiving this prize, I will perform:

_____

_____

_____

Remember; always pay your vows (especially to the Lord). If you can't pay it, then don't say it.

Your vows should be
Prepared, Printed, Proclaimed and Posted.

Your vows (promises) are important. Record and review them until they become ingrained in your spirit. Remember, your word gains value when you keep it!

Your word appreciates (gains value) when you keep it.
Your word depreciates (loses value) when you break it.

Stay Perfected – Stay Pure

The Bible, in the book of 1 Corinthians 6:19, teaches that *your body is the temple of the Holy Spirit of God who lives in you*. It goes on in the next verse to state …*you must honor God with your body*.

That tells us that we have a responsibility to stay loyal and to stay pure. How do you honor God with your body? You honor Him when you take good care of your body, which is His property.

Have you ever had somebody visit you at your home and leave it a mess? Have you ever loaned something valuable to a friend and have it returned dirty or broken? Of course. We all from time to time experience somebody who has absolutely no respect for our possessions. When they disrespect your possessions they, in effect, disrespect you. How does that make you feel?

Now, think about The Refiner's claim that your body is His temple. He instructed you to honor it. Are you that person who leaves it a mess? Are you that person who returns it dirty or damaged?

If that's you, fix it! Do not leave God's property in worse condition than the way you received it. You received it, at birth, perfected and pure. You damaged it through drug abuse and addictions. But, through **The Refinement Process**, your heart can be restored to perfection and purity.

To say, *Stay Perfect and Stay Pure,* will not win the battle. Catchphrases are not enough. To win this campaign requires your unwavering commitment. Remember the price that The Refiner paid for your ransom. He suffered extreme persecution, pain, and a torturous execution to pay for your rescue and redemption.

He paid a debt He did not owe so that you could receive salvation you did not deserve. Recognize that now you are His. Use your life to honor Him. Honor Him in your body, your mind and your spirit.

Never forget, you don't have to do it alone. You have with you always a supernatural power available to you. The Refiner is always there to help you maintain. Make a commitment to God to strive to stay perfect and pure. He is committed to you; after all, He also wants His temple clean!

This may all seem impossible; you are right. For mankind it is impossible, but with God all things are possible. Impossibilities are no match for The Refiner's supernatural power which He makes available to you.

Let's shift gears once again with an Action Step.

Recommitment Step 3 – My Stuff; Your Stuff

There is a problem when your stuff isn't really YOUR stuff. It might be misappropriated stuff (stolen) or it might be stuff borrowed and never returned. Either way, it is stuff that is not rightfully yours. It is difficult starting a new life with stuff that belongs to someone else.

So, for this Action Step you will jettison (get rid of cargo); other people's stuff. Start by taking inventory of all your stuff. Make note or tag stuff that you recognize are not yours: public library books from 1995, Nikes that still have the price tag on them, power tools with your neighbor's initials engraved in the side; you know the stuff. Separate other people's stuff from your stuff.

NOTE: Obviously, if you are doing this in a small group setting you do not have *stuff* with you. If that is the case, use the follow spaces to make a list of things in your possession (at home). Make a distinction between Your Stuff and Other People's Stuff that you possess.

My Stuff	Other's Stuff

Now take one (or all) of the following actions:
1. Return borrowed stuff
2. Restore stolen stuff
3. Repay your debts
4. Make good on past promises

Do these things and you will feel so much better about your own stuff and about yourself. Other people will feel better about you too! It is a win, win, win situation. There may be stuff that you cannot return, restore or repay. In those cases, maybe you can compensate in other ways using your time or talent in service to them.

Do your best to return, restore, repay and make good on past promises. Obviously, these actions will take some time to complete; so, get started and get it done.

The Depth of your Commitment will determine
The Height of your Success.

Notes

Notes

The Reemergence Phase

Reemergence: the act or process of emerging again; Evolution - the appearance of new properties or species during development.

The time has come for you to get up and get started in your new life. But be cautious; do not start something new the same old way! Start your new life with a new and improved perspective, a new mindset where drugs do not fit.

In the Reemergence Phase, you will learn how to maintain your sobriety. You do that by staging your new life, removing the old patterns of behavior and replacing them with new, positive behaviors and habits.

You are being totally transformed from the inside out. You are emerging, out of the cocoon, as a fully developed, beautiful butterfly, a colorful Monarch. Now that you have come out, there is no longer a need to crawl; it is time to fly. Stretch out your wings; you are going up. Reemerge better than ever.

Do not return to that old mess which was your old life. Do not go back to that old environment. Jonah never returned to the belly of the fish. When Jesus arose from the dead, He never returned to the empty tomb. The butterfly doesn't go back to the cocoon out of which it came. Neither does the butterfly associate with caterpillars. Get out and fly with other butterflies!

> *You have set yourselves a difficult task, but you will succeed if you*
> *persevere; and you will find a joy in overcoming obstacles.*
> Helen Keller

From this Reemergence Phase you will be recognized as a new creation, born anew. Talk with The Refiner every day. Daily tell Him,

"O Lord, my Refiner, transform my tastes. Adjust my appetite for things that are wholesome. Reform my soul. Purge me of the unrighteous pleasure of addictions. Let me not be entertained or be amused by sinful acts. I

renounce spiritual wickedness that has influenced my tastes. Apply Your perfect strength to my every weakness."

Always remember, you did not rescue yourself, Jesus The Refiner rescued you. Be grateful to Him for saving you. Be thankful to Him for your new purified life. Now that you are being delivered from drug dependency, remember to glorify God.

> *I am forgotten as a dead man out of mind:*
> *I am like a broken vessel.* Psalms 31:12

Visibility Restored

As an addict, you were out of sight. You were hidden; you were invisible. Why? Because nobody really wanted to see you. You were too big a mess. You messed over people. Family, neighbors, friends, co-workers, they were all stained by your addictions. Consequently, many of them erased you from their sight.

Now that you are purified, you will shine so bright, people will notice you. The new you!

It is wiser to change surroundings than
to let surroundings change you.

People will recognize a change in you. Some people will like the change, some people will hate it. Those who like your positive change will be those who will be an encouragement to you. They will be supportive of your growth and development.

Try to surround yourself with those people. This will probably require that you surround yourself with a new circle of friends, letting go of old counter-productive relationships.

People that hate the positive changes in you will want you to go back to your old ways. They will miss having you there with them. Avoid past addicted acquaintances by any means necessary.

No matter how much you love them, or enjoy being around them, druggies will not fit into your new life, so don't even try to make room for them.

At this stage of your development, you are not ready to debate or defend your new drug-free life. Some of your old friends and associates will not understand it and many of them will not like the fact that you have escaped from their disastrous fate.

If possible, simply avoid them. Give yourself plenty of time to grow and develop in your new life. The Refiner has given you a better way to live. Enjoy it and make the most of it.

Control Your Environment

The federal government has a department for which its sole mission is to protect the environment. The Environmental Protection Agency (EPA) monitors, regulates and enforces laws concerning Land, Air, and Water Pollution.

If the federal government considers it important to protect the environment, why is it that people do not think it important enough to protect their own personal environment? I do not mean your land, air or water; I refer to the protection of your mind, heart and soul.

You should establish your own **Personal Environmental Protection** policies (PEPs). You must diligently protect your own personal environment. You must monitor, regulate, and enforce the laws concerning your life space, your personal environment.

Just to be clear, I am not referring to air or water pollution. By **Personal Environmental Protection**, I am referring to your living and working space. You may ask, "How do I protect my own environment?" You must first identify the pollutants in your space. Pollutants come in the form of polluted pressures, polluted people or polluted paraphernalia.

> Polluted Pressures – Weaken your Character
> Polluted People – Corrupt your Thinking
> Polluted Paraphernalia – Disable your Actions

Polluted Pressures

Daily, you face external forces that put downward pressure on you. I call them Polluted Pressures. These hindering forces are all around you, and, if you are not cautious, they can negatively impact your new refined life. There is a proverb which states

Above all else, guard your heart, for everything you do flows from it.
Proverbs 4:23 (NIV)

Polluted Pressures are exhibited in the music, movies, television, and negative talk that surround you each day. These are vehicles which regularly deliver filth to your heart.

Lyrics, which stir up your lusts; movies, which glorify alcohol and drug abuse; discussions, which ridicule and revile God; the Polluted Pressures are all around you.

God instructs you to be aware of what you permit in to your heart. You need to place a guard at your Eye-Gate and your Ear-Gate. Think about it: Much of what you see and hear is polluted. Those things will defile your character.

Jesus The Refiner purified your heart and He is in the process of perfecting you. He expects you to keep it clean. Therefore, it is crucial that your **Personal Environmental Protection** policies include your policy to identify and avoid Polluted Pressures.

One of the practices, which will help you to protect your environment, is attending church. Through regular church attendance you can be strengthened in your relationship with God.

Ask The Refiner for help in this area. He will lead and guide you in all truth. If regularly attending church is your course of action, make sure that you go to a Bible believing, Bible teaching church. Look at their Mission Statement to understand what they believe and teach.

Polluted People

All of us rate the people in our lives from those who matter the most to us to those who matter the least. You have social circles that surround you: immediate family, close relatives, neighbors, coworkers, close friends and casual acquaintances.

There are social circles which include people who influence you. You also have social circles which include people whom you influence.

Not everyone in your life wants to see you succeed.

Polluted People want you to be like them. They want you to join their misery and their misfortunes. They want you to live by their polluted standards. Therefore, they will do all that they can to keep you contained and contaminated by their corruption.

Consider the illustration of crabs in a barrel. Some of the crabs try to escape from the barrel to freedom. But just as one crab reaches the rim of the barrel, with his escape assured, his fellow-crabs reach up and pull him back down.

You have friends, family and acquaintances who are not ready for you to escape. Believe it! Deal with it! There are people, no matter how close they are to you, that no longer fit in your new life.

Do not make room for them. Remove all traces of the Polluted People from your life, not only physically, but also on all social media platforms (Facebook, Twitter, Instagram, Google+ and all your contact lists). Do it today!

Polluted Paraphernalia

As a drug addict, you had certain items on hand to help you get high. Drug paraphernalia such as: ZigZag rolling papers, smoke pipes, bongs, roach clips, coke spoons, syringes. The best way to define paraphernalia is *tools of the trade* or items used to accomplish a task.

Therefore, Polluted Paraphernalia are those tools from your past that are still on hand and available to help you go back to an addicted life.

Maybe you no longer have a junk drawer full of drug paraphernalia. But, what things from your past life are still lingering? What stuff is still hanging around? It might be an old T-shirt (especially the one with the marijuana leaf), old CDs or DVDs, old posters or artwork, old books or incenses.

Polluted Paraphernalia serve as reminders of past addictive activities. The problem is that they also can serve as tools available to return to those past addictive activities. The time has come to dump the tools of your past pollution.

Polluted Pressures, Polluted People and Polluted Paraphernalia - The Refiner will help you to create a life where those things do not fit. The great thing is that He will help you to be your own Personal Environmental Protection Agent.

He will help you to control your environment. He does that by helping you to identify and replace the pollutants with purity. After all, He is The Refiner!

> Pure Pressures – Empower your Character
> Pure People – Challenge your Thinking
> Pure Paraphernalia – Enable your Actions

Now let's take some time to examine your Personal Environment. You will be looking at your space where you live. You will be identifying the atmosphere (Pressure); the influences (People) and the objects (Paraphernalia) that make up your environment.

Once those people and things are identified as being harmful, then you can begin to think about healthful replacements. All of this will go into creating your **Personal Environmental Protection** policy.

Reemergence Step 1 – Identifying My Personal Environment

Below you will see three separate tables, each having two columns. There is a table for Pressures, a table for People and a table for Paraphernalia. To start, just work on just the left-side columns in each table.

1. In the first table, make a list of Polluted Pressures (music, movies, television, negative talk, etc.)
2. In the second table, make a list of Polluted People (family members, friends, neighbors, coworkers, etc.)
3. In the third table, make a list of Polluted Paraphernalia (things that represent your past addictive life.)

Now that you have identified what is polluting your space, identify how to clean up your environment. To do that you must reduce or eliminate the pollutants by replacing them with pure choices.

In the right-side columns below, make your pure list. For each item on your three polluted lists - Pressures, People, Paraphernalia - identify a pure replacement:

1. Replace Polluted Pressures with Pure Pressures (beautiful music, movies, TV, etc.)
2. Replace Polluted People with Pure People (successful people, teachers, mentors, new friends and sponsors)
3. Replace Polluted Paraphernalia with Pure Paraphernalia (objects of beauty, things that inspire and help you to life clean)

Polluted Pressures   **Pure Pressures**

Polluted People   **Pure People**

Polluted Paraphernalia	**Pure Paraphernalia**

Take the necessary time to think through and write out these lists. It is important to complete these lists. They must be completed before you can take the next Action Step.

Now let's create your own **Personal Environmental Protection Policy** (PEP).

Reemergence Step 2 – Creating My PEP Policy

With the three tables in the last Action Step you identified the pollutants that need to be removed and replaced. The columns on the left contain your pollutants; the columns on the right contain your pure replacements.

The concept here is to <u>prevent</u> and <u>prohibit</u> those Pressures, People and Paraphernalia that are polluted; and at the same time, <u>permit</u> and <u>promote</u> all that is pure. This will help you to establish your **Personal Environmental Protection Policy** that you can use to monitor and reinforce your development.

From the left-hand columns (the pollution side) of each of the three tables, select three pollutants that you want to prevent/prohibit. List them in the PEP box below

From the right-hand columns (the pure side) of each of the three tables, select three pure items that you want to permit/promote. List them in the PEP box below.

My Environmental Protection Policy

Part 1 – Eliminate Pollutants

To ensure a healthy, drug-free environment this policy is being enacted to prohibit polluted pressures, people and paraphernalia

Therefore, effective immediately The Refiner and I prevent the following pollutants:

Polluted Pressures _____

Polluted People _____

Polluted Paraphernalia _____

To enforce this policy, I will be on my guard to prevent these pollutants in my environment. Where they may persist, I will call upon The Refiner to be my very present help in being rid of them.

Part 2 – Embrace Purities

Also, effective immediately The Refiner and I promote the following purities:

Pure Pressures _____

Pure People _____

Pure Paraphernalia _____

To enforce this policy, I will welcome and permit these purities in my environment. I will call upon The Refiner to be my very present help in maintaining my pure environment. Amen!

The goal here is to live and thrive in an environment where drug do not fit. With this Action Step you are enacting a policy to protect your new addiction-free environment. But, it is up to you to enforce it. You enforce your new PEP through the supernatural power which is available to you. That is with the help of Jesus, The Refiner.

NOTE: For those of you who are now incarcerated, understand that no matter how bad your present environment, there are no walls that can imprison you tighter than addictions. A lengthy prison sentence will demoralize your mind, but addictions destroy your everlasting soul. Jesus, The Refiner and **The Refinement Process** can help you to be free anywhere, especially in prison.

A man may imagine things that are false, but he can only understand things that are true, for if the things be false, the apprehension of them is not understanding.
Sir Isaac Newton

Successful Living Through Refinement

Before you begin a course of action, always find out what The Refiner wants you to do. Ask Him for guidance. If you try to get results based on your own understanding, then you will get limited success. You need the understanding of the Lord, your Refiner, to achieve success without limits.

Trust in the LORD with all your heart; and lean not on your own understanding.
In all your ways acknowledge Him, and He shall direct your paths.
Proverbs 3:5-6 (NKJV)

To live a successful life, you will need guidance and direction that exceeds your own understanding. That can be frightening and unnerving because you might think that to succeed you must have all the answers. But, that is your old, faulty way of thinking, and it couldn't be farther from the truth.

To succeed, you need a new and improved way of thinking. The previous verse holds the key. *Do not lean on your own understanding*; acknowledge Jesus, The Refiner, and He will direct your successful path.

Successful living through Refinement requires you to know what to do, know how to do it, and then to do it. If you don't know what to do nor how to do it, you cannot succeed. You might ask, "How do I get the answers?" You get the answers when you ask God.

If you don't know what you're doing, pray to the Father. He loves to help.
You'll get his help and won't get condescended to when you ask for it.

James 1:5

God will talk to you and give you help.

Most praying people know how to talk to God. They regularly load Him up with their To Do Lists and their Wish Lists; "Lord, I need this," or, "Lord, do this for me."

Very few people know how to listen to God. He really does want to talk to you; and better than that, He wants to talk *with* you! Prayer is not meant to be a monolog (one person talking), it is supposed to be a dialog (two people holding a conversation).

All throughout the Scriptures you can see where God listened and replied to His people. He held conversations with ordinary people. God wants to know your thoughts and He wants you to know His thoughts.

Here is another Action Step to help you to apply this truth. To make the most of this Action Step, you must first realize that you can talk to The Refiner and He will talk to you.

NOTE: Since this Action Step is so personal, it should not be a part of any small group or Bible Study. If you are using **The Refinement Process Workbook** from a group study, use this Action Step for homework to be completed prior to your next meeting. At that time participants can be allowed an opportunity to share their individual findings.

Reemergence Step 3 – Inquiring of the Lord

Here are seven questions that can change your life. Actually, the questions will not change your life - But, the answers to these questions and your application of these truths can absolutely change your life.

Spend some quiet, uninterrupted time with the Lord. Find a place where you will not be disturbed. Take with you a pen and paper (or a recording device) to jot down the answers. Now ask the Lord each of these questions and expect Him to answer you.

1. What do You want to say to me; what would You have me to know?

_____

_____

_____

_____

_____

2. You have a good purpose for me; what do You want me to know about it?

_____

_____

_____

_____

_____

3. You have a good plan for my life; what do You want me to know about it?

_____

_____

_____

_____

_____

4. What hinders my relationship with You and how do I deal with those things?

_____

_____

_____

_____

_____

5. Is there anyone that I need to forgive, just like You forgave me? Help me to forgive.

_____

_____

_____

_____

6. What are my wrong beliefs that You want me to be aware of? What is the truth that You want me to replace them with?

_____

_____

_____

_____

7. How can I begin to redeem the wasted years of my life, beginning today?

_____

_____

_____

_____

Be patient. This will take time and it need not be rushed. Relax and talk to the Lord the same way that you talk with your best friend. Listen to what He says and write it down.

Once you have received answers to each question, begin to find ways to apply these truths to your daily life. This is an amazing process and you should make it a regular part of your relationship with The Refiner.

Make this a lifelong practice; let this develop into a good habit throughout your life. It is thrilling to know that the Lord, your Refiner, hears and personally responds to you.

Notes

_____

_____

_____

_____

_____

_____

_____

_____

_____

_____

_____

_____

_____

_____

_____

_____

_____

_____

_____

_____

_____

_____

_____

Notes

Welcome to Your New Life

Congratulations!

Welcome to your new life! I know it was not easy and it was not always pleasant, but you have successfully completed **The Refinement Process Workbook**. Step out in to an addiction-free life. You earned it. There is a vast, vibrant future that awaits you.

The Refinement Process is here to assist you in making the steps which lead to your new life. Make this process a part of your new life style. Incorporate the lessons learned here into your everyday mindset.

Live free, my friend. Live your life to the fullest. Because of The Refiner, you can have the abundant life which He promised: Love, joy, inner peace, patience, kindness, goodness, gentleness, faithfulness and self-control. These are called the *Fruits of the Spirit*, and every day they are all available to you.

The Refiner's Benefit Package

In your new life, always remember it was Jesus, The Refiner that rescued, redeemed and refined you. The Refiner will continually give you direction. He will daily give you His benefits.

The Refiner's Benefit Package

Bless the LORD, O my soul,
and forget not all his benefits   Psalms 103:2

Psalm 103: 3-5 lists a personal Benefits Package for those who make The Refiner Lord of their lives. These six benefits are promised to you.

The Refiner:

Forgives all my Iniquities

Heals all my Diseases

Redeems my life from Destruction

Crowns me with Lovingkindness and Mercies

Satisfies my mouth with Good Things

Renews my Youth

These are benefits which nobody can take away from you. Recognize that there will always be sin, sickness and death in this world (into each life some rain must fall), but, your personal Benefits Package puts you at an advantage over every sin, sickness and disease (anything that would come against you to destroy you).

These benefits give you an assurance that The Refiner raises you up and esteems you, making sure that you have all that you need to live in this world as a new creation.

Make note of your personal Benefits Package; write it and post it in a place where you are continually reminded of His promises to you. It will give you confidence as you live your new drug-free life.

Now you are prepared to go out into this world and make a difference. The difference you make in this world will bring glory, honor, and pleasure to The Refiner.

The Refiner not only purifies you, He perfects you.

Now that you have been refined (purified and perfected), live your life to the fullest. Set new goals or resurrect past goals that got derailed over the years. Go out and tell others about **The Refinement Process**. Tell them about what The Refiner did for you. Remember to give the Lord all the credit for your refinement.

Jesus, The Refiner, still wants to be part of your new life. You still need to make Him a part of your new life. His promise to you is that He is as close to you as the mention of His name. Whenever you face difficulties and disasters, call on Jesus, The Refiner. He is available to help you.

With this welcome also comes warning.

Warnings for Your New Life

Beware!

Although your future is bright, you will still have challenges awaiting you on the road ahead.

> *Habit, if not resisted, soon becomes necessity.*
> Augustine

Life will hand you many opportunities to fail. Hurdles, pitfalls and traps all await you in your new life. Trials and temptations are all part of life, and, sometimes, they might get the best of you (or more likely, the worst of you).

Recognize that you have been cleansed by The Refiner. Every day you will need Him to help keep up pure. Realize that there are impure spirits that still desire to infect your purified heart. See what The Refiner said about your soul and the enemies of your soul:

> *When an impure spirit comes out of a person, it goes through arid places seeking rest and does not find it. Then it says, 'I will return to the house I left.' When it arrives, it finds the house unoccupied, swept clean and put in order. Then it goes and takes with it seven other spirits more wicked than itself, and they go in and live there. And the final condition of that person is worse than the first. That is how it will be with this wicked generation.*
> Matthew 12:43-45

Don't let anyone sell you a bill of goods. Your new life will not always be a bed of roses. There will be times when the past will look tantalizing.

There may even come a time when you succumb to your past unrighteous desires. We live in a cursed, sin-filled world, so do not be dismayed if you find yourself on Relapse Road. Whenever you fall, get up and be refined again.

I firmly believe that **The Refinement Process** will work for all addictions: gambling, pornography, tobacco smoking, alcohol excesses, foul language, and on and on.

The same five phase process, Reflection, Repentance, Redemption, Recommitment and Reemergence, can help you to be free from anything that has control over your life. If you apply **The Refinement Process**, you will come forth as pure gold.

Relapse Road

(an excerpt from the book, *The Refinery, Overcoming Addictions Through The Supernatural Power Available To You*)

> *The LORD upholds all that fall, and raises up all those that be bowed down.*
> Psalms 145:14

Relapse Road is not a narrow, unpaved path. It is a broad, smooth, well-lit street. It is the way that leads back to the bondage of addiction. It is not hidden away, far from view. It is a major highway. It runs right alongside Main Street. I know, because I was on it. And if you are not cautious, you will find yourself there, too.

The Refiner took steps to ensure that you would be well protected and safe. You see, you are a finished work; you are His Masterpiece! So, He put certain safeguards in place to help keep you secure and successful.

After achieving so great a victory as your refinement, you will still be tempted to set foot on Relapse Road. Some of you will avoid the temptation and go on to live successful lives. Some of you will surrender to the temptation and stumble on to Relapse Road. That is what happened to me; I stumbled and fell back. It can happen, but do not despair.

> *We all want progress, but if you're on the wrong road, progress means doing*
> *an about-turn and walking back to the right road; in that case, the*
> *man who turns back soonest is the most progressive.*
> C.S. Lewis

Sign Posts on Relapse Road

Just like any major street, there are many signs posted on Relapse Road.

Street Signs: Generally posted on each corner to identify the name of the street on which you are traveling and all cross streets. On Relapse Road, you are continually reminded where you are. Just look up at each intersection, there is a sign, **Relapse Road**. Your head and your heart continually remind you, *this is not where I want to be.*

Caution Signs: Posted to warn travelers of possible dangers along the way, such as: Construction Ahead, Slippery Pavement, Detour Ahead, and Do Not Pass. On Relapse Road, the caution signs were placed there by The Refiner (against the strong objections of our enemy, Satan). Wrong Way! Do Not Enter! Take Next Exit! These signs are reminders that where you are heading is extremely dangerous and disastrous. These signs are not to be ignored!

No Parking Signs: Posted to indicate that there is no space for you to pull over and pause. This street is too busy, with too much traffic. Do not interfere with the flow of traffic. Do not park here, keep moving! That is what Satan wants from you. No Parking, No Standing…just keep moving on Relapse Road.

On Relapse Road, there are two signs that are sure indicators of an unsuccessful future and a disastrous destiny. The signs are **One Way** and **Dead End**. The One-Way sign is an arrow which points the way to your destruction. The Dead-End sign indicates that at the end of this road, there is death and destruction.

> *The thief comes only to steal and kill and destroy...*
> John 10:10a (NIV)

The two signs that you will not see on Relapse Road are **Speed Limit** and **STOP**. The enemy knows that if you slow down or even stop, then you might realize that you are heading for disaster. He wants you to continue farther and farther down this road as fast as you can. No slowing and no stopping there!

But, The Refiner is always available to bring you back.

**You are never too far gone that you cannot repent
and be rescued once again.**

False Justifications

One of the most powerful weapon in Satan's arsenal is deception. Whereas the truth shall make you free, deception shall entangle and enslave you. Whenever the enemy can get you to forget the truth and embrace the lie, he has deceived you; once deceived, you are headed for a fall.

Lucifer's fall from heaven began with self-deception. He mistakenly believed that he could establish his throne higher than God's throne. Adam and Eve's fall from grace began with deception. They mistakenly believed that when they ate the forbidden fruit they would be like God. By the way, they were already like God; He had already created them in His image and likeness!

Deception is also the belief that you are doing something right, when in reality, the thing you are doing is wrong.

On Relapse Road, the deception the enemy uses are through false justifications. Justification is the action of showing something to be right or reasonable. Therefore, false justification is the action of showing something to be right or reasonable, when in reality, it is false. In the case of relapse, the false justifications can be stated as follows:

> Well, I already failed, so I might as well keep going this way.
> Once an addict, always an addict!
> There is no hope for me. I'll never change.

Nothing could be further from the truth! Let's explode each of these false justifications with the true justifications of God's Word:

> *For a just man falls seven times, and rises up again...*
> Proverbs 24:16a

> *Therefore, if anyone is in Christ, he is a new creation; old things have*
> *passed away; behold, all things have become new.*
> 2 Corinthians 5:17 (NKJV)

> *The steps of a good man are ordered by the LORD, And he delights in his way. Though he fall,*
> *he shall not be utterly cast down; For the LORD upholds him with his hand.*
> Psalms 37:23-24 (NKJV)

Finally, this is your last Action Step.

Triggers, Traps, Temptations and Triumphs

A gun cannot fire unless you pull the trigger. The traps are continually baited and setup for your arrival. Temptations will try to invade the eye-gate and the ear-gate of your heart. But, you have access to a supernatural power which will cause you to triumph. It is your higher, greater power.

Temptations, when we meet them at first, are as the lion that roared upon Samson; but if we overcome them, the next time we see them we shall find a nest of honey within them.
John Bunyon

Curiosity Killed the Cat, It Can Harm You Too

Curiosity is a powerful mental force. It can motivate you to seek out positive, uplifting things or negative, unrighteous things. For me, it was usually the latter. I could always tell when I was being tempted to go astray and sin. It was when I was curious about something that God told me was off-limits.

When God, through His Word of instruction and correction, sets a limit, it is for our protection. In this sinful world there are many baited traps and many slippery slopes. They are ingeniously placed by our enemy to cause us to fail. We are safe if we stay inside the boundaries which God places around us.

Satan uses curiosity to get you to question and eventually doubt God's Word. It always starts with a question, followed by a suggestion of a better way (than God's Way). You can see an example of this in the Bible when the serpent in the Garden of Eden used deception against the woman, Eve. He baited the trap with curiosity. You can see this exchange in Genesis 3:1-5.

One day he asked the woman, "Did God really say you must not eat the fruit from any of the trees in the garden?" (That was his question which raised her curiosity).

"Of course we may eat fruit from the trees in the garden," the woman replied. "It's only the fruit from the tree in the middle of the garden that we are not allowed to eat. God said, 'You must not eat it or even touch it; if you do, you will die.'"

"You won't die!" the serpent replied to the woman. "God knows that your eyes will be opened as soon as you eat it, and you will be like God, knowing both good and evil." (That was his suggestion of a better way).

And with that questioning and suggesting, the seed of curiosity was planted in Eve. The Bible says *she was deceived.* She looked upon the tree and the forbidden fruit with a curious new desire to taste it. She ate it and gave it to Adam to eat. Curiosity won the day.

Satan uses curiosity to lure you into lusting for things which will defeat and destroy you. Through curiosity, the enemy attempts to lure you to go outside of God's protective boundaries. When he succeeds, and you stray off limits, that is called a *trespass*. Unrighteous curiosity can be the onramp to Relapse Road.

Do not let curiosity get you off track. Turn your curiosities toward the things of The Lord. He will protect you and cause you to triumph.

A man may imagine things that are false, but he can only understand things that are true, for if the things be false, the apprehension of them is not understanding. Sir Isaac Newton

Final Action Step – Take another "Selfie"

Here we go again. On your mobile device or tablet, take a second selfie. As we learned in the first phase, pictures have a way of showing the true you. It is said, "one picture says a thousand words."

Now, compare this selfie with the selfie you took at the beginning of this course.

This is your before and after comparison. Look at the before photo. Does it reflect your thoughts, feelings and attitude in the beginning? Look at the photo you just took. Has anything changed in your appearance?

Some people actually see a change. But, even if you don't see any change on the outside, you know something has changed on your inside. If you completed this course, then there is a good possibility that your heart has changed.

Fallen, but not Flattened

If you do fall, you do not have to stay fallen. We fall down, but we get up again. Remember The Refiner's promise, **For a just man falls seven times, and rises again.** It does not surprise Him when you fall. Toddlers fall many times until they learn to balance themselves and walk. Just keep getting up. If you fall, do not allow yourself to be flattened. GET UP!

It is extremely important that you not linger or loiter on Relapse Road. The quicker you exit, the quicker you can be rescued, restored and refined. There are some things to recognize whenever you fall.

Take some time to reflect and recognize:

Where am I? – You are on Relapse Road, returning to your past life of addictions.

How did I get here? – You were deceived and tempted. You believed the deception and you succumbed to the temptation.

How do I get out of here? – You must go back to the Repentance Phase, repent and be restored. Leave your guilt, shame, and anger behind; be refined once again.

Recommendations to Avoid Relapse Road

- Read the Holy Bible daily.
- Regularly attend a Bible believing, Bible teaching church.
- Tell people about your deliverance from addictions.
- Pay it forward. Help someone you know who is struggling with addictions.
- Pray and give thanks to The Refiner, the Lord Jesus.

Notes

_____

_____

_____

_____

_____

_____

_____

_____

_____

_____

_____

_____

_____

_____

_____

_____

_____

_____

_____

_____

_____

_____

_____

_____

Notes

Specialty Pages

The Refinement Process

Reflection Phase - Seeing Present Reality

Repentance Phase - Making a Directional Decision

Redemption Phase - Restoring Ownership

Recommitment Phase - Pledging Purity

Reemergence Phase - Becoming Visible Again

The Refiner

He sat by the fire of seven-fold heat,
As He watched by the precious ore.
And closer He bent with a searching gaze
As He heated it more and more.
He knew He had ore that could stand the test
And He wanted the finest gold,
To mold as a crown for the King to wear,
Set with gems of price untold.
So He laid our gold in the burning fire,
Though we fain would have said Him, "Nay."
And He watched the dross that we had not seen,
As it melted and passed away.
And the gold grew brighter, and yet more bright
And our eyes were so dim with tears.
As we saw the fire, not the Master's hand,
And questioned with anxious fear.
Yet our gold shone out with a richer glow,
As it mirrored a Form above
That bent o'er the fire, though unseen by us
With a look of infinite love.
Can we think that it pleases His loving heart
To cause a moment of pain?
Ah, no, but He saw through the present cross
The bliss of eternal gain.
So He waited there with a watchful eye,
With a love that is strong and sure,
And His gold did not suffer a bit more heat
Than was needed to make it pure!
Source Unknown

Salvation & Serenity Prayers

Prayer for Salvation

Lord Jesus, my Refiner, I know that I am a sinner, and I am sorry for my sin. I repent of it and I turn to You by faith right now. I believe that You are the Son of God. Thank You for dying on the cross for me and paying the price for my sins. I ask You to come into my life now and be my Rescuer and my Refiner. I surrender myself to You. Refine me and help me to live my life for You. Thank You, Lord. In Jesus name I pray. Amen.

Prayer for Serenity

*God, give me **Grace** to accept with serenity*
the things that cannot be changed,
***Courage** to change the things*
which should be changed,
*and the **Wisdom** to distinguish*
the one from the other.
Amen.

My Personal Vision Statement

I _____ *am fearfully and wonderfully created by God to look like Him and to act like Him. He created me for His pleasure.*

I _____ *am created to be productive and powerful.*

I _____ *will be fruitful, multiply the resources of my fruitfulness, then use those multiplied resources for the benefit of other people.*

My Refiner is always with me and He always points me to the right path. Through Him, I _____ *make use of the supernatural power available to me.*

My Environmental Protection Policy

Part 1 – Eliminate Pollutants

To ensure a healthy, drug-free environment this policy is being enacted to prohibit polluted pressures, people and paraphernalia

Therefore, effective immediately The Refiner and I prevent the following pollutants:

Polluted Pressures _____

Polluted People _____

Polluted Paraphernalia _____

To enforce this policy, I will be on my guard to prevent these pollutants in my environment. Where they may persist, I will call upon The Refiner to be my very present help in being rid of them.

Part 2 – Embrace Purities

Also, effective immediately The Refiner and I promote the following purities:

Pure Pressures _____

Pure People _____

Pure Paraphernalia _____

To enforce this policy, I will welcome and permit these purities in my environment. I will call upon The Refiner to be my very present help in maintaining my pure environment. Amen!

The Refiner's Benefit Package

Bless the LORD, O my soul,
and forget not all his benefits
Psalms 103:2

Psalm 103: 3-5 lists a personal Benefits Package for those who make The Refiner Lord of their lives. These six benefits are promised to you.

The Refiner:

Forgives all my Iniquities

Heals all my Diseases

Redeems my life from Destruction

Crowns me with Lovingkindness and Mercies

Satisfies my mouth with Good Things

Renews my Youth

Recommendations to Avoid Relapse Road

Read the Holy Bible daily.

Regularly attend a Bible believing, Bible teaching church.

Tell people about your deliverance from addictions.

Pay it forward. Help someone you know who is struggling with addictions.

Pray and give thanks to The Refiner, the Lord Jesus.